Vishnu and Sheshnag the Serpent

Shubha Vilas

Om
KIDZ
An imprint of Om Books International

Sheshnag was the first born son of Sage Kashyap. He had inherited all his father's simplicity and righteousness.

Therefore, he was upset with his wicked mother Kadru and his brothers for deceiving their stepmother Vinata and making her their slave.

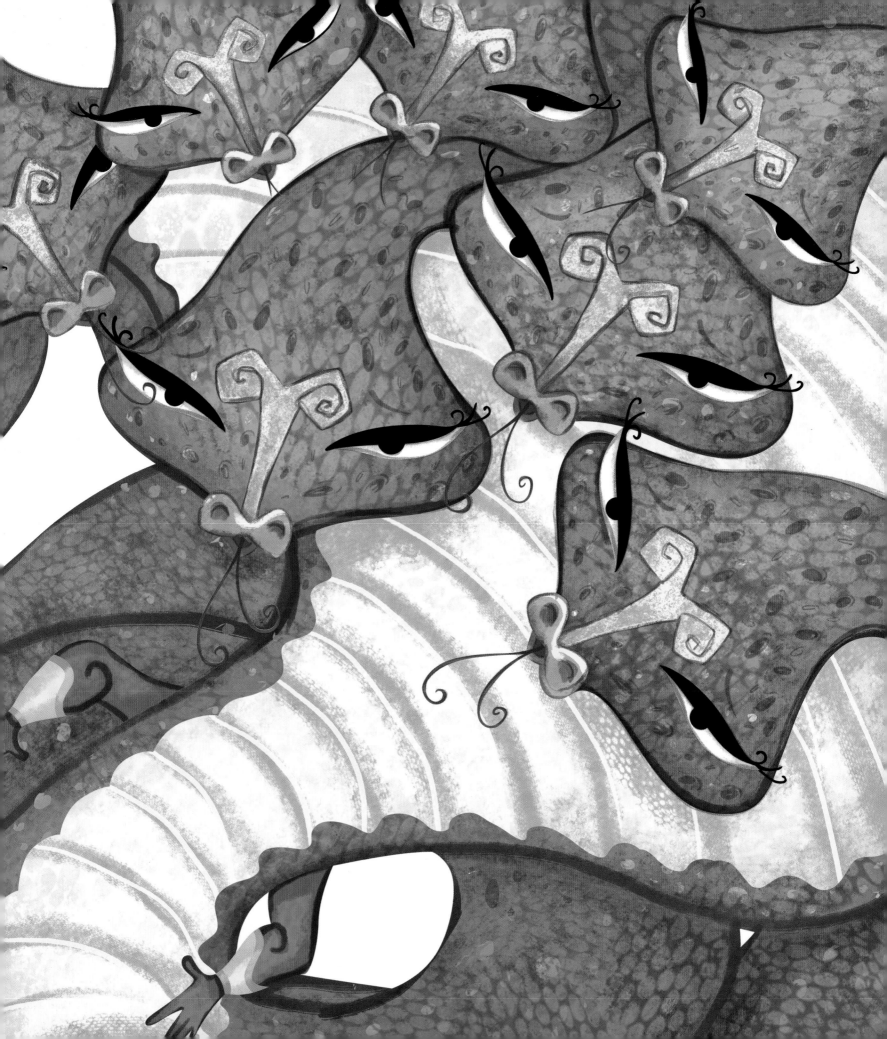

Once, after a bet with Vinata regarding the colour of the divine horse Uchaishravas's tail, Kadru asked her thousand snake sons to wrap themselves around the tail to make it appear black.

By cheating Vinata, Kadru lost the affection of Sheshnag. He was tired of the wily and evil deeds of his mother and other brothers. They were grossly unfair.

Sheshnag thought about how he could help Vinata. Kadru and his brothers refused to listen to any logic or appeal. Disappointed, Sheshnag left home. He wanted to go as far away as possible from his selfish family.

His heart desired to be on the path of goodness and spirituality and to help others. With so many thoughts churning in his hood, tears rolled down his eyes.

The gentle soul slithered into the Himalayas. Here he decided to immerse his mind in meditation. Maybe, when he calmed down, he would know what to do in life. Giving up food and water, he only survived on air.

Slowly, he started to lose weight day by day. One day, Brahma got worried about Sheshnag's health and came to speak to him. He could see that Sheshnag needed help.

Brahma gently asked, 'Why are you punishing yourself like this? Tell me what is it that your heart desires? I want to help you.'

Sheshnag saw the Father of the World, Brahma standing in front of him. He said, 'My evil mother and brother see nothing wrong in cheating Vinata and my cousin Garuda. I am so unhappy that I want to give up my life.'

Brahma was touched by the noble serpent's words. 'I know you are right. But don't worry. I will take care of Kadru and your brothers. Why don't you do something for the world? Tell me what your wish is. I will grant you a boon.'

'I wish to follow the path of truthfulness. I wish to help mankind. I wish to serve Lord Vishnu.'

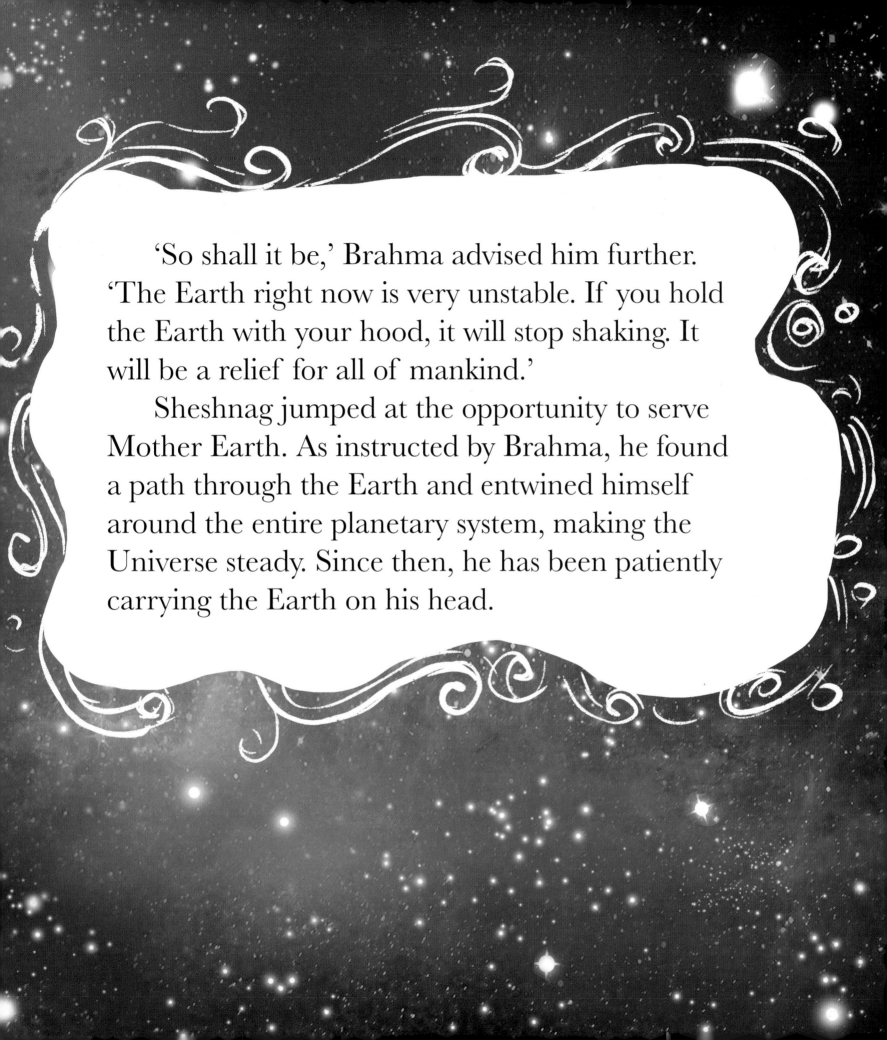

'So shall it be,' Brahma advised him further. 'The Earth right now is very unstable. If you hold the Earth with your hood, it will stop shaking. It will be a relief for all of mankind.'

Sheshnag jumped at the opportunity to serve Mother Earth. As instructed by Brahma, he found a path through the Earth and entwined himself around the entire planetary system, making the Universe steady. Since then, he has been patiently carrying the Earth on his head.

It is said that if Sheshnag moves even a little bit, the tectonic plates shift, creating earthquakes. By holding the Earth firmly, he not only serves all of mankind, but also Lord Vishnu.

He is the bed on which Vishnu rests in the milky ocean. Vishnu granted him a boon that he would always accompany him wherever he went. Sheshnag appeared as Lakshmana along with Rama, and as Balrama along with Krishna.